THE BOY WHO LISTENED TO FIRE

Published by
Our Sunday Visitor, Inc.

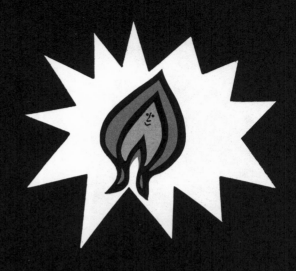

THE BOY WHO LISTENED TO FIRE

by Patricia Collins

Michael sat and watched the logs
burning brightly in the fireplace.
The flames flickered and sputtered.
Some were yellow, some were red.
Michael could feel their warmth
on his face.

Sometimes, on special occasions,
Michael and his mother and father
ate their dinner by candlelight.
The little flame on each candle
was not very bright
and not very hot.
But the flame was bright enough
to make the dinner special,
and it was hot enough
to melt the wax
and make it drip down the side of the candle.

The flame on the candles
came from the flame on the matchstick
that Michael's father used to light them.

Michael knew that somehow –
though he did not know how –
the flame sat at the end of the matchstick,
waiting to be called.

One afternoon, Michael was helping
his mother to make pudding for supper.
She put some flour
and some milk into a pot on the stove.
She turned on the flame
under the pot.
Michael watched the flame licking
the bottom of the pot.
His mother added some other things
to the milk and flour and stirred
them all together.
Michael asked, "What makes the pudding?"
His mother said, "The heat makes the pudding.
The heat from the flame."

"Well," said Michael, "then what makes the flame?
Where does it come from?"
"The flame," said his mother, "comes from a tiny flame,
which is always burning right here in the middle of the stove.
It's called a pilot light.
It lights the burners when I want to cook."

Later that evening,

after the dishes had been washed and put away,

Michael went into the kitchen.

He turned off the light,

and in the darkness he could see the pilot light

glowing in the middle of the stove.

The pilot light was very small,

smaller than the flame on a matchstick,

smaller than the flame on a candle.

It was a very quiet flame.

It did not dance around much –

except when Michael was talking to it!

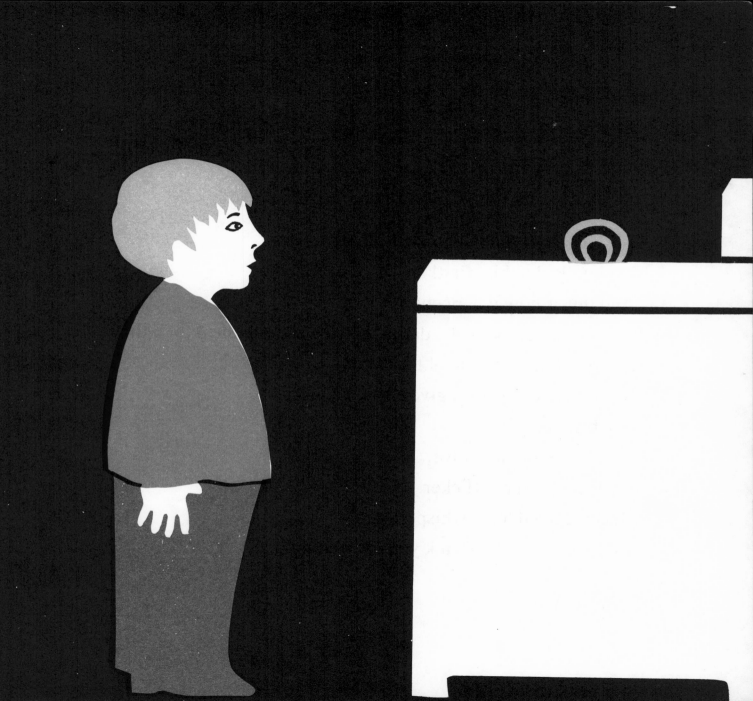

Yes, Michael did talk to the little pilot light,

but it talked to him first!

And this is how it happened.

As Michael stood in the dark kitchen watching the pilot light

glowing in the middle of the stove,

he thought he heard it give a sputter,

or a hiss, or a click.

The flame did not move.

The flame did not flicker.

But it seemed to be whispering,

"Hello, Michael. Thank you for visiting me."

Michael was very excited.

"Hello," he said. "Who are you?"

And this is what the flame said:

"I am a part of fire," said the little flame.
"I share fire with all the other flames
everywhere in the world . . .

''We flames are like a fire people.

Our job is to help humans like you.

We warm up their houses and cook their food.

No matter where people live,

we are there to help.

We heat their water and burn their trash.

We light the candles on birthday cakes, too,

and that's something we especially like to do.

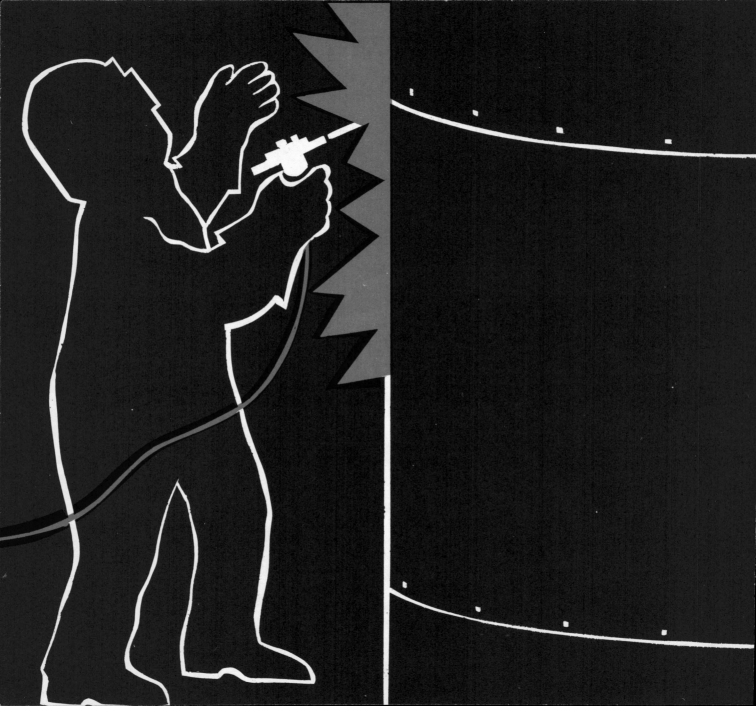

''When the welder lights his torch,
we go to work to help him fasten steel plates together,
making space rockets and bridges,
bicycles and wagons.

"Without our help, the steel makers
would not be able to melt iron and other metals.
People would have a hard time making tools
and large buildings.

"Perhaps you have seen a glass-blower at work.
The glass-blower needs us to help him heat the glass
so that it is soft enough to shape into
beautiful bowls and glasses.

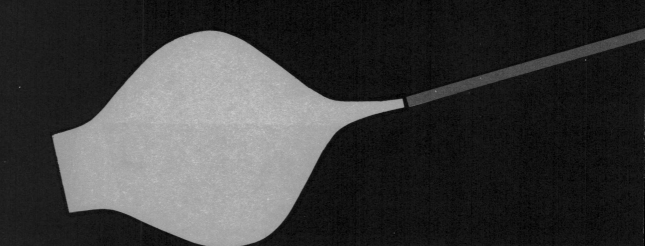

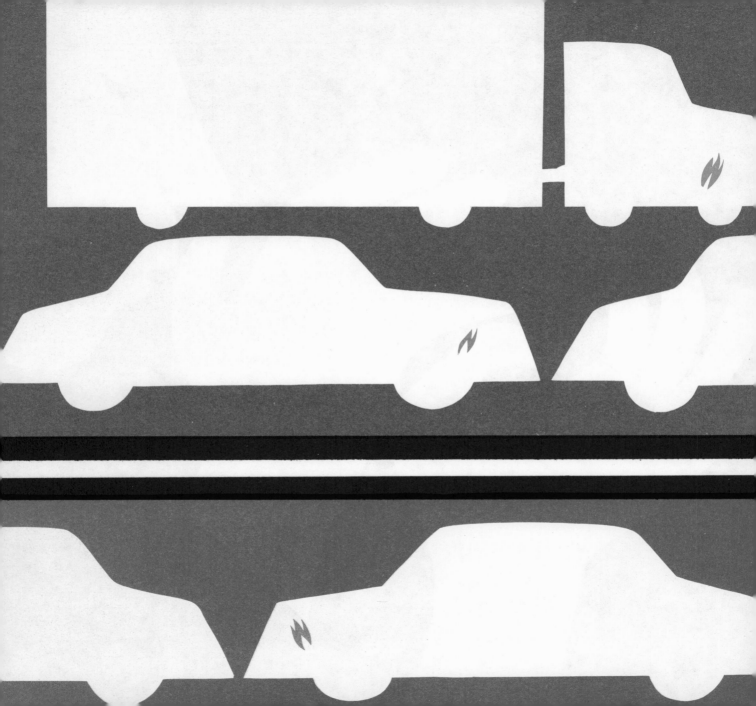

"And the cars and trucks and buses
that drive along your roads
would not go anywhere if it were not
for the tiny flames called sparks
inside their engines.

"So you see," said the pilot light,
"we flames are at work for you in many ways."

"Yes," said Michael, "I see what you mean."
Just then, he heard his mother calling him.
It was time for bed.

A few days later, Michael was watching television.
He was watching a program about the sun.
He learned that the sun was a giant ball of fire
and that all the stars in the night sky were
giant balls of fire, too.
The stars looked much smaller than the sun
because they were much, much farther away.

When Michael asked the pilot light about the sun and stars,

the little flame whispered to him,

''Yes, that's right, the sun and stars are fire also.

The sun gives light and warmth to the earth.''

''But what about the moon?'' asked Michael.

''The moon is not fire,'' said the flame. ''It is the sun's mirror.''

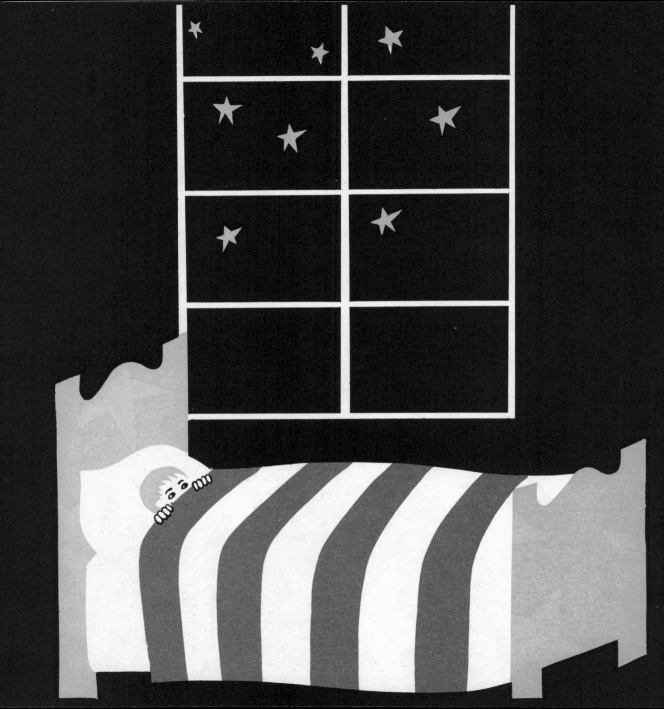

That night, when Michael went to bed,

he could not sleep.

He looked out of his window at the stars

and wondered what it would be like

if the earth had no fire.

''There would be no bonfires in autumn,'' he thought,

''no fireworks on the Fourth of July,

and no way to pop popcorn in fireplaces.

There would be no warm sunshine,

and the earth would be always dark.

There would be no moon, no stars in the night-time sky,

no candles on birthday cakes and no matches to light them with.

And there would be no pilot light, either!''

Michael was feeling very sad
from thinking about what it would be like
to live in a cold, dark world,
under a cold, dark sky.
And he knew then how important fire was in his life.

He got quietly out of bed and went
into the dark kitchen.
The little pilot light was glowing
in the middle of the stove, as usual.
And Michael was very happy to see it.

He whispered to the little flame,
"Goodnight."

The little flame gave a little sputter,
and then Michael thought it began to sing: –

"The sun is overhead by day,
The stars again by night:
Their flames are working to convey
To you their warmth and light.

"And here on earth we flames can share
Our warmth and light with you.
We serve you here, we serve you there,
We serve the whole day through!"

The little flame gave another little sputter,
and then it was quiet and still again.

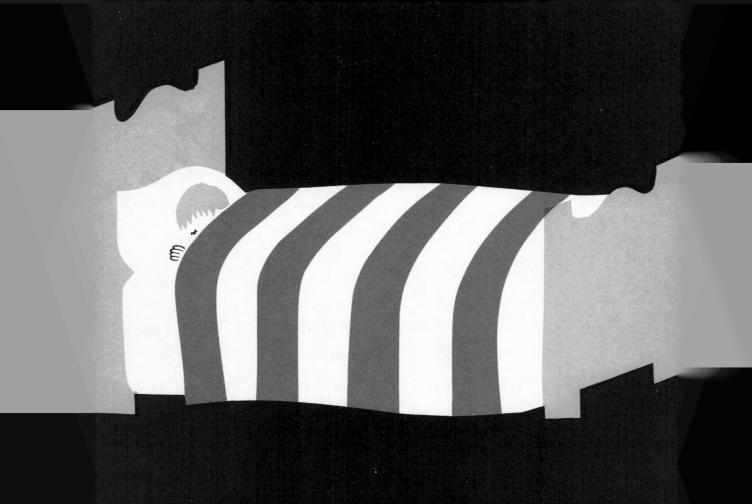

Michael went back to bed,
closed his eyes, and fell right asleep.